D0767116

We constantly travel the globe to discover new gemstones.
Scan this QR code on a mobile device to read the latest news.

The Little Book of Gemstones (S)
www.tggc.com

All enquiries should be directed to:
The Genuine Gemstone Company Limited, Unit 2D
Eagle Road, Moons Moat
Redditch, Worcestershire, B98 9HF

ISBN: 978-0-9559972-8-0
Published by The Genuine Gemstone Company Limited
Designed by The Genuine Gemstone Company Limited

THE LITTLE BOOK OF GEMSTONES

S

By Steve Bennett

INTRODUCTION

Welcome to the world of Mother Nature's treasures: a world full of colourful locations, colourful people, colourful stories and, of course - colourful gems.

This series has been written in an A to Z encyclopaedic format, so that you can dip in and out at your leisure. Whenever you come across a new gemstone or hear someone mention a jewellery term that you have not heard before, you can easily use these books to quickly find out more.

Steve Bennett

Sancy Diamond

One of the most historically fascinating Diamonds ever found has to be the Sancy Diamond. The history of this gem started over 600 years ago, when it was reputed to have been discovered in the fabled mines of Golconda, India.

The Sancy Diamond was once the largest Diamond ever discovered, but since Diamonds were discovered in South Africa in the late 1800s, its size is no longer quite as significant. The gem's outline shape is comparable to a cross between a shield and a pear cut stone. What makes it so unusual is that its profile is the same shape either side of the girdle.

The Sancy was believed to impart invincibility to anyone who wore it. The Diamond has been worn by several members of France's royalty. Elizabeth I pursued the Diamond for decades. The gem has also funded many battles; after being stolen from the Louvre it was sold to help pay for Napoleon's war efforts. There is so much history and fascination surrounding this Diamond that we would highly recommend Susan Ronald's book "The Sancy Blood Diamond".

Sapphire

Sapphires are known and revered the world over for their beauty and mystery. In many ancient cultures this gem has been admired not only for its elegance but also for the magic and good luck often associated with it. In western civilisations the Sapphire has long been the traditional stone of choice to set alongside Diamonds for a man wanting to express his love and commitment to someone special.

For over a thousand years, Sapphires have enjoyed a close association with royalty. The unquestionably exquisite and perfectly turned out Mrs. Simpson received many gems from Edward VIII. Her collection included incredible Emeralds, vivid Rubies and large, flawless Diamonds; however she always maintained that her favourite gemstone was Sapphire. Indeed, she was so proud of one bracelet, designed by Van Cleef and Arpels, that apparently she asked her tailor to shorten the sleeves of all her dresses and blouses so that everyone could see her Sapphires. In the 1980s, resurgence in the popularity of Sapphire rings occurred shortly after Prince Charles purchased a stunning Ceylon Blue Sapphire ring as Princess Diana's engagement ring.

Sapphires come in a range of colours, from summer sky blues to jet black, colourless and all colours in between. Sapphire is a member of the Corundum family; pure Corundum, known as White Sapphire, is colourless. The wide array of differing hues seen in Sapphires is due to the presence of different impurities found in their crystal structure. Blue Sapphires are formed due to the presence of titanium. Chromium trapped inside Corundum allows us to enjoy Pink Sapphire and in larger quantities gives us the Ruby (when Corundum is red it is renamed Ruby instead of Sapphire). When admiring a Sapphire, turning it back and forth will allow the light to travel through the gem and display even more colours; this beautiful array of colours emitted as the gem is moved is known as pleochroism.

In addition to being surrounded by many myths and legends, this gemstone also enjoys one of the richest histories. In antiquity Persians believed that Blue Sapphires were actually chips from a huge pedestal that supported the Earth, the reflections of which coloured the sky. In the Middle Ages it was thought to be an antidote against poisons and to possess a magical power to influence the spirits.

12

It is also mentioned numerous times in the Bible: "Under his feet was something like a pavement made of Sapphire, clear as the sky itself" (Exodus 24:10). "In the second row a Turquoise, a Sapphire and an Emerald" (Exodus 28:18). "Sapphires come from its rocks, and in its dust contains nuggets of Gold" (Job 28:6). "His body is like polished ivory decorated with Sapphires" (Song of Solomon 5:14). "O afflicted city, lashed by storms and not comforted, I will build you with stones of Turquoise, your foundations with Sapphires" (Isaiah 54:11). "You were in Eden, the garden of God; every precious stone adorned you: Ruby, Topaz and Emerald, Chrysolite, Onyx and Jasper, Sapphire, Turquoise and Beryl. Your settings and mountings were made of Gold; on the day you were created they were prepared" (Ezekiel 28:13). "The foundations of the city walls were decorated with every kind of precious stone. The first foundation was Jasper, the second Sapphire, the third Chalcedony, the fourth Emerald" (Revelation 21:19).

Sapphire and its sister, Ruby, share a common attribute. Although Ruby has been unearthed in several countries, there is one country where its source is most highly prized: Burma. Likewise, though Sapphires are unearthed in countries as far afield as Madagascar,

14

Australia, Thailand and China, the most highly regarded Sapphires come from a country known as "gem island": Sri Lanka. These Sapphires, especially when blue, are known as Ceylon Sapphires (Sri Lanka was previously known as Ceylon) and command incredibly high prices per carat, particularly when they have not been heat-treated. The only region to take the limelight away from Ceylon was Kashmir in India, where in the early 1900s a deposit was discovered that yielded superb violet-blue Sapphires that were described as velvet in appearance. The Songea region of Tanzania has provided one of the more recent discoveries of a kaleidoscope of stunning Sapphires. This gem is the birthstone of September and is associated with the Zodiac sign of Taurus. It is also the gift for the 5th, 45th and 70th anniversaries. Its hard crystal structure measures 9 on the Mohs scale, making it incredibly durable. When set in a ring or pendant, and given proper care, it should continue to shine for thousands of years to come.

Sapphire Feature
Evaluating Sapphires

The most attractive Sapphires are those that are a pure blue. Whilst pure body colours are desirable in most gemstones, those whose colour is a primary colour such as the red of Rubies and the blue of Sapphire, really can demand a price premium when their hue is pure. That said, some gem collectors prefer their Sapphires to have a purple hue of approximately 10 to 15% within the gem.

In terms of saturation you will sometimes see a greyish mask (see mask heading to get a better handle on saturation and masks) and if the gem lacks life this could be the cause. In terms of tone it depends on your preference between

17

18

lighter cornflower blues and deeper royal blues. Unfortunately today we see far too many Sapphires on the market, especially from some locals in China and Thailand, where the tone is almost 100% (i.e. black).

Another important evaluation criterion for both members of the Corundum family (Sapphire and Ruby) is whether the gem bleeds or not (see bleeding heading). When some Sapphires are worn indoors under incandescent light, they can often lack sparkle, their tone seems to diminish and the gem almost fades, but take them back outside and they instantly revitalise. Not all Sapphires bleed in the same way and the level of their bleeding depends on their chemical composition.

Probably more than any other gem (with the exception maybe of Pearls), Sapphires have often been valued more for their origin than their beauty. But to paraphrase the most legendary of all gem explorers ever, George Kunz, great gemstones can be found in any location and poor ones can be unearthed at locales that are renowned for the most prized. You are just as likely to find a poor quality Sapphire in Kashmir as a stunner in China.

The key evaluation criteria for Sapphire as with all coloured gems remains the

vividness of its colour, its transparency, its clarity and its cut. Then of course, if you are faced with a choice of two similar gemstones from different locales, you might choose to acquire the one with an origin that is renowned for producing great pieces of that gem variety or you may even choose the other piece that is the shining star of an under performing locale.

Let's discuss the properties that are typically associated with each location, but please do bear in mind the above comments. These are the summary of the huge amount of books I have read, yet my experience is more in line with the views of George Kunz in that quality and appearance can vary from location to location. My opinion is based primarily on the gems that flow through my sorting office in Jaipur and those that we sell through our various channels. It is also based on the fact that when I was recently in Zambia I witnessed from one small location in a mine, no bigger than three foot square, a miner unearthed the most stunning, clear deep green Emerald, only five minutes later to find two more pieces that were dull and lifeless. The difference can be narrowed even further: it's not just the country, the region, the particular mine, the area within the mine that makes a difference, but the portion of the rough that your gem has been cut from. Only yesterday I was in my cutting facility where we were cutting some of the finest Amethyst rough we have ever purchased: after making the first slice (a slice is the first cut made to gemstone rough, performed to remove a part of a gem with a big fracture or large feather inclusion) we were left with two totally different grades.

So the information below is more related to the typical types of Sapphires found in each location. It's more like saying you will find more Brits in Britain, more Thais in Thailand and more Indians in India. But if you look in today's cosmopolitan cities, you will

realise this type of view is no longer completely valid. It is also important to point out that with today's modern gemstone treatments such as colour diffusion, these differences are less reliable than they use to be in terms of arriving at a dependable origin based on appearance alone.

Kashmir Sapphire
Regarded by many as the finest Sapphires in the world, they were first discovered in 1879 in the Padar region of Kashmir in Northern India after a landslip allegedly uncovered their occurrence. The Kashmir Sapphire has been known for over a century as "the Jewel of India". Unfortunately,

after just a few years of mining, the area became unworkable due to the area being in the middle of a politically unstable area and one fraught with conflict. The matter worsened in 1947 after the partition of the subcontinent, and Kashmir, which is located in the Himalayas some 4500 meters above sea level, has been war torn ever since. So whether it is a result of the conflict or the fact that the mine was depleted within just a few years of its discovery is still not completely understood and remains one of the most talked about topics in gem circles.

Even though the driving force behind its true rarity is not known, at an auction at Christie's in 2007 a 22.66 carat Kashmir Sapphire set in a gold pendant fetched a price of $3,064,000. This equates to around £85,000 per carat!

Kashmir Sapphires are renowned world wide for their almost sleepy appearance. The reason for this is that they have thousands of microscopic inclusions: these cannot be seen by the naked eye, but under a microscope can normally be identified. Also known as flour, these inclusions diffuse the light, providing the Sapphire with its legendary sleepy appearance. The Kashmir Sapphire typically is a very pure blue, with few secondary colours and has a tone of 70 to 80%.

Ceylon Sapphire

Made famous in the UK after Princess Diana was given a large Ceylon Sapphire in the centre of her engagement ring and subsequently re-emerging when given to Kate Middleton on her engagement to Prince William, Ceylon Sapphire is today regarded as the finest Sapphire still being mined in any commercial quantity.

Its hue varies from a deep royal blue to a lighter blue (known as cornflower) and purplish blue. The gem often will have some inclusions and colour zoning, therefore it is often heat treated to produce a gem that is more marketable to the masses. Its tone ranges from approximately 30 to 75% for desirable gems.

Madagascar Sapphire

There are various grades of Sapphire coming out of Madagascar presently. Those from Ilakaka tend to have a nice open colour which has a bluish purplish hue, whilst those from other areas I have seen on the island such as Andranondambo tend to have a darker tone. Some pieces coming from the Swiss Banque Mine in Ilakaka, a mine run by John Noel whom I have met several times whilst in Madagascar, often produce pieces that are on par with Sapphires heralding from Burma, Kashmir and Ceylon. Occasionally you will find unusual shaped inclusions in Sapphires from this region and experts have discovered that these are normally either Calcite or Apatite crystals.

If you are thinking about acquiring a Madagascar Sapphire then take a look at the Madagascar heading in our 'M' book.

Kanchanaburi Sapphire

Famous for its vividly coloured blue Sapphires, the mines at Kanchanaburi and Bo Ploi (also spelt Bo Ploy) also produce the occasional grass green and sunflower yellow Sapphires, as well as their world famous Black Spinel. The mines are situated in a jungle valley to

the north west of Bangkok; the area is a very popular tourist spot and its bridge was featured in the war film "The Bridge on the River Kwai".

The main Sapphire mines are some twenty miles north of the main town. The first discovery was made in 1918 and within months thousands of miners started digging to make their fortunes. Within a very short period, the mines were all depleted. In the late 1970s, the gem was once again rediscovered, but this time with JCBs and modern equipment, mine owners were able to dig deeper. By the late 1980s they had created possibly the largest alluvial deposit Sapphire mine on the planet.

Reportedly they had to excavate an average of 19 tonnes of soil to uncover just one carat of gem quality Sapphire! Today, the mines are almost completely exhausted and very little mining is taking place: I met with one local who told me that current miners are having to sift through approximately 50 tonnes of soil to find a single piece of Sapphire.

The quality from the mines vary from heavily zoned pieces, to pieces that are as open in colour and share a similar clarity to Ceylon Sapphires. In terms of tone, I have seen Bo Ploi Sapphires vary from 60% to 90% tone. In terms of saturation, Sapphires from the region can be amongst the best on the planet. Whilst Kashmir Sapphires are famed for their silky sleepy appearance, those from Kanchanaburi can sometimes look slightly milky.

The GIA class Sapphires as a "type II" gemstone, meaning that they normally will feature inclusions. It is for this reason that Kanchanaburi Sapphires are nearly always heat treated. This method, perfected in Thailand centuries ago benefits Sapphires from this region in two ways: it reduces the impact of the colour zoning and lessens the visual impact of the inclusions.

Australian Sapphire

Unearthed in New South Wales and Queensland, Australian Sapphires have a tendency to be more of a greenish blue than a pure blue when extracted from the ground. With modern heat treatment techniques, Aussie Sapphires are easily transformed into a more pure blue and then sometimes they are mis-sold by ill-informed or unscrupulous dealers as Ceylon Sapphires.

Chinese Sapphire

As with most gemstones that originate from China, the amount of data and information we are aware of is very limited. What we do know is that most of the gem quality Sapphires mined in the country come from the Shandong Province, which is situated on the East coast of the country. As the gem is mined in basaltic or magmatic deposits, they tend to have a tone that is very dark, often in excess of 95%. Under a microscope if you ever find small, dark orange inclusions in your Sapphire, there is every chance that these are due to the presence of uranpyrochlore crystals which are often found in Sapphires from the Shandong Province.

**Sarah
Bennett
Collection**

SARAH BENNETT

GEMSTONE
JEWELLERY

Sardonyx

Throughout the ages there have been many myths, legends and folklore surrounding the spiritual qualities of Sardonyx (also known as Banded Agate). Romans soldiering into war would wear the stone, engraved with a picture of Mars (god of war), believing it would bring them courage in times of doubt.

The name Sardonyx itself is an amalgamation of its composition, the two minerals 'Sard' and 'Onyx'. During the Renaissance in Europe it was believed that this stone gave speakers eloquence when talking. In Ancient Greece people used to carve them into the shape of scarab beetles, a mythological creature that was believed to eat people! The gem also has many links with royalty and it is said that Queen Elizabeth I gave the Earl of Essex a large Sardonyx Gold ring as a present.

Sardonyx is the reddish brown coloured member of the Agate family and it normally has varying coloured layers and a vitreous to waxy lustre. The main use of Sardonyx throughout the ages has been to make carved cameos (a carving made out of a gemstone).

Today Sardonyx is mined in various locations around the world, however in years gone by it was considerably rarer and more valuable. There was even a time when it was worth more than Gold! Most of the world's supply is mined in the Sardonyx Mountains in India and it is generally agreed that this is where the highest quality Sardonyx comes from. The gem is also found in Russia, Australia, Brazil and Madagascar.

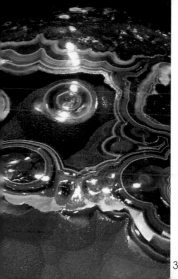

Saturation

Saturation is one of the three criteria we use to measure colour. It's often overly complicated in other industries and yet I feel it does not need to be.

Although there is a saturation chart, the easiest way to grasp saturation is simply this: is the hue (colour) vivid or dull? Take a look at the photo for Azurite in the first book, its colour is incredibly vivid; it has a vivid saturation. Have a look at Blue Chinese Sapphire, it is more dull; it has little saturation. Both these gems have the same hue: they are both blue, but one has high saturation and one has low saturation. If you want

36

to go to an extreme, a hi vis, Day-Glo yellow cycling vest most definitely has a vivid saturation, whereas yellow butter, especially after it is spread on your toast, will appear more dull.

The Azurite is vivid; it has no other feeling of colour. What less vivid colours tend to have is either a brownish or greyish tinge to the colour. It's not always instantly noticeable but it tends to be there (obviously with Smokey Quartz or Grey Moonstone you can't use what I am about to describe). This brown or grey tinge is often referred to as a mask. Different gemstones will tend to have different masks. All Sapphires that are not vivid in colour will have a tinge of grey and never brown. However, if a Rubellite's colour is anything other than bright red, if you study it closely you will notice a brownish mask. The more dull the colour, the more brown you will see.

Hailing from Sarwar in Rajasthan, India this devastatingly
beautiful Iolite is a collectors dream. A gemstone that is steeped
in history, it is a rare find indeed to discover a deposit that
produces these deeply saturated rich violet gems.

Each incredible gemstone will grace your collection with its own
individual personality as it plays with light and displays a subtly
different colour from every angle. To achieve this beautiful effect
it is vital that the lapidarist orients the gem properly when cutting,
for this reason you can be assured that your Sarwar Iolite has been
cut by one of our most skilled craftspeople.

Sarwar Iolite

Iolite takes its name from the Greek "ion" meaning "violet flower" and many legends surround its uses throughout the ages. Your Sarwar Iolite comes from one of the greatest locations ever discovered for this gemstone and is totally natural and free from treatments.

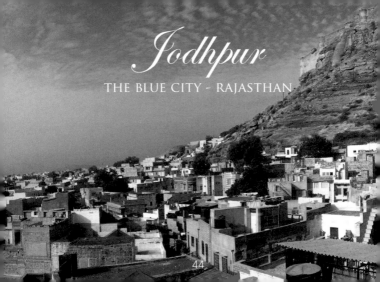

Jodhpur

THE BLUE CITY - RAJASTHAN

*Sarwar is located just to the East of the fabulous Blue
City of Jodhpur in the Thar Desert. Built in the shadow
of the Mehrangarth Fort, this historic city played a
major part in establishing trade routes throughout
India for silk, copper, dates and coffee.*

SarwarSolite

Iolite is highly pleochroic, meaning that different colours can be seen when you view the gemstone from different angles. So strong is the phenomenon within this Iolite that it can show strong royal blues from one angle and subtle glacial blues or even sunrise yellows from another. It is this attractive quality that has led Iolite to be known as the Water Sapphire.

Iolite is considered to be a visionary gem by crystal healers promoting clear thoughts and heightening intuition. It is also believed to help you express your true self and break free from the expectations of others.

"One who walks in another's tracks leaves no footprints."
Ancient Proverb

Sarwar Solite

Known as the 'Vikings' Compass', Iolite was used by the early explorers to navigate the open seas of the Atlantic Ocean and beyond. Due to its legendary pleochroism a piece of Iolite would be set on a ships deck, the navigator would stare at the stone and correct the ships course if the colour of the gemstone changed.

Sarwar Iolite is one of the most beautiful examples of this fascinating gemstone ever discovered. The beautiful primary violet blue hues mellow with tender softness as you view the gemstone. It is an amazing gemstone that has helped shape world history through exploration, a fabulous natural treasure which will add interest and beauty to any jewellery collection.

54

Scapolite This family of gemstones is identified primarily by its unusual crystal structure which is known as tetragonal dipyramidal (the only two other minerals on Earth that share this structure are the even lesser-known Powellite and Scheelite). Its structure provides a prismatic shape and its name is derived from the Greek word "scapo" meaning 'rod' or 'shaft'. Normally found in colours similar to Rose-de-France Amethyst or Lemon Quartz, Scapolite is a gemstone that is highly prized by both gem collectors and jewellery connoisseurs. When the gem's appearance is similar to Amethyst it is thought to help the wearer make important decisions, whereas the more lemony, citrus colours are said to provide relief from aches and pains.

Historically the gem was known as Chrysolite, which was a name given to many greenish yellow gems including Peridot (see also the Breastplate of Aaron). During the last century, the gem has also been known as Wernerite, Mizzonite, Dipyre and Marialite. Today its new name Scapolite is widely recognised throughout the gem industry.

Some believe Scapolite was first discovered in Burma, but others maintain it was originally found on

Egypt's St. John's Island (once known as Topazios and today renamed Zeberget) in the Red Sea. The confusion surrounding its discovery is likely to be due to its previous identification as Chrysolite.

In addition to purple and yellow, the gem can be discovered in various attractive colours including pinkish purple, blue, grey and colourless. In its transparent form it is often brilliant cut and when discovered translucent it is normally cabochon cut, which occasionally enables the gem to display chatoyancy (a cat's eye optical effect). The finest samples on the market today are from the Umba River area of Tanzania; other locations for the gem include Australia, Madagascar and the USA.

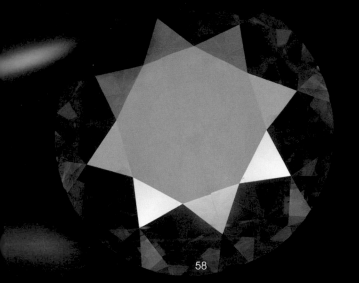

Scintillation

Very similar to lustre and brilliance, scintillation is used to describe the optical effect seen in gems such as Diamonds, where an area of light on a polished facet seems to flash on and off as either the gem or the light source moves. I often refer to scintillation as the lighthouse effect. The GIA (Gemological Institiute of America), who invented the four 'C's as a way of measuring the quality of Diamonds, use scintillation as one of the seven criteria for assessing the quality of a gem cut.

Scintillator Brilliant Cut

In a world where everything is done in a rush, where time is money, where value seems to dominate over quality, you will be pleased to know that there are still a few Lapidarists around that view their craft more as a hobby and challenge, than a financially rewarding job. Just like great painters, those who view Lapidary as an art, have the wonderful ability to create masterpieces that are truly spectacular.

Take the classic brilliant round cut, it has become our staple diet in the gem world ever since Tolkowsky developed it in 1919.

But when time and profit is put to one side for a moment, then imagine what happens when a gem cutter enlarges the table facet and adds around 80 small triangular and kite shaped facets to the crown? Then by turning the gem over, makes time to patiently do the same to the pavilion. The result is a gemstone that offers incredible scintillation (the effect seen when you slowly rock a gem backwards and forwards and the entire facet on a crown flashes on and off like a lighthouse) and yet still retains its internal brilliance.

This cut is only suitable for gems with great clarity, as its larger table facet hides nothing; it's also a great cut to use if you want to show off strong vivid colours within a gem. Due to the complex arrangement of facets, don't expect to see it on gems weighing less than two carats and do expect to pay a little more than a standard round brilliant cut gem.

62

Scribbling Ring

Exchanged by lovers in the 16th century, "Scribbling Rings" were set with a Diamond faceted not with a table facet, but with a sharp point, which was then used to engrave messages of love on glass.

Queen Elizabeth I and Mary Queen of Scots were two of the most famous scribblers: Sir Walter Raleigh was said to have scribbled upon his Queen's window: "Fain would I rise but that I fear to fall." Elizabeth's reply was: "If thy heart fail thee, do not rise at all."

Today, after a long absence, scribbling rings are returning to fashion; however, this time it is coloured gemstones that are being used. Those buying these pieces are usually unaware of the history behind the cut of the gem and are likely to wear the piece as a fashion statement, rather than a writing tool!

Having said they were popular in the 16th century a Scribbling Ring was recently discovered in Leicestershire, England, which experts have dated back to the early medieval period, possibly the 11th century. A report in The Times newspaper on 21st of August 2008 states that a Mr Stevens, who was using a metal detector, found the Black Diamond ring in a local field and experts believe it once belonged to either the Church or royalty.

Semi Precious

In the 1700s and 1800s the phrase 'precious gems' was applied to the three most desirable gems of the period: Ruby, Sapphire and Emerald.

In the early 1900s Diamond also earned the title 'precious gemstone', whilst all other gemstones became known as 'semi precious'. Today the term 'semi precious' is frowned upon within the industry, as many gemstones such as Paraiba Tourmaline, Alexandrite, Sphalerite, and several others, often fetch substantially higher prices per carat than those previously belonging to the exclusive 'precious gemstone' club.

The International Coloured Gemstone Association (ICA) goes as far as to say, 'The problem with semi precious, and the reason why the jewellery industry has banned its use, is that it is quite misleading. Rubies, Emeralds, and Sapphires can sell for less than $100 per carat and a fine Paraiba Tourmaline, for example, can sell for $20,000 per carat. That seems pretty precious, doesn't it?' Incidentally the French word for gemstones is "pierres précieuse."

Setting

A setting is the mount in which gems are set into rings, earrings, pendants and bracelets. There are many different styles of settings used in modern jewellery making; the more common ones being illusion setting, prong setting (also known as a claw setting), pave setting, channel setting, tension setting, milgrain setting, bezel setting and invisible setting.

It is important to consider the setting when buying jewellery set with gemstones. Always remember that Gold and Silver are relatively soft metals and therefore only a small amount of pressure applied to a prong setting in the wrong direction can easily alter its shape. Simply by catching a prong on a fibre as you remove a jumper could bend a prong and therefore I recommend that prong set pieces are quickly checked prior to putting them on, to ensure that the gem is not loose.

One well-known setting for rings is the Tiffany setting (named after the famous jewellers who first made it popular), this is a 4 or 6 prong setting that elevates a solitaire gem above the band of Gold or Platinum. If a gem is completely enclosed, as in a bezel setting, it is referred to as a closed setting; the term open setting would apply to prong set gems.

Serpentine Although we tend to refer to Serpentine as a gem type, it is in fact a gem family featuring several different minerals including Antigorite, Chrysotile and Lizardite (named after the Lizard Peninsula in Cornwall where it was first discovered). As Serpentine is relatively soft (2.5 to 4.1 on the Mohs scale), gem-quality material is normally kept for Gem Collectors rather than being set into jewellery. Unfortunately for those of us that live in the UK, all gem-quality Serpentine is Antigorite, rather than the Lizardite which is found in plentiful supply in the South West of the country!

In some countries, Serpentine is dyed and sold as "Korean Jade" or "New Jade". In times gone by in New Zealand, the Maori people use to carve ornaments out of the mineral, as the gem is relatively soft and easy to work with.

Similar to the likes of Chalcedony and Agate, Serpentine is a microcrystalline gem and therefore is normally opaque to translucent in appearance. Colours range from whiteish grey, to yellowish green, to very dark brown, almost black.

The Serpentine we currently have in our vault is from Afghanistan, but it can also be discovered in Cornwall, England, Ireland, California, Canada and Norway.

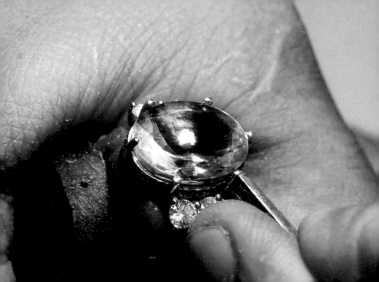

Shank

When you hear the word shank in relation to a ring, it is usually referring to the piece of metal that runs around the ring from one shoulder to the other. It is important that the shank is well finished and slightly rounded at the edges, so that it is comfortable to wear. If 18k Gold or higher is used, it is important that the shank is sufficiently deep; otherwise the Gold's relative softness could result in the ring bending and losing its shape. Unfortunately, with Gold being such an expensive metal, this is not always the case. With stronger metals such as titanium, it is less critical to have a deep shank.

Freeform Small
(less than 6 sides)

Freeform Large
(less than 6 sides)

Shapes Although the whole industry blurs the boundaries between shapes and cuts, I have always been taught that in the strictest sense, the cut of the gem refers to either the quality of the faceting or the shape and arrangements of the facets. Whilst the shape refers to the outline shape of the gem when viewed from the top. The shapes below are the main recognized shapes, onto which Lapidarists will apply facets and at which point we can start discussing cut.

In this section we have listed 42 of the most commonly used shapes for gemstones. These shapes represent the view from the table.

Bullet

Star

Heptagon

Fan

Window

Nonagon

Rhomboid

Navette Oval

Undecagon

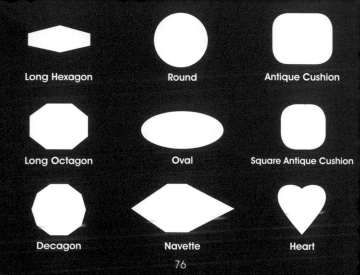

Long Hexagon

Round

Antique Cushion

Long Octagon

Oval

Square Antique Cushion

Decagon

Navette

Heart

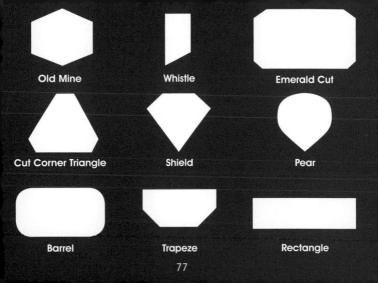

Old Mine

Whistle

Emerald Cut

Cut Corner Triangle

Shield

Pear

Barrel

Trapeze

Rectangle

Square

Kite

Epaulette

Baguette

Keystone

Hexagon

Lozenge

Cushion Triangle

Triangle

Octagon

Square Emerald

Seminavette

Pentagon

80

Shiva Eye

Also known as Shiva Shell or sometimes Pacific Cat's Eye, Shiva Eye is a stunning natural gem whose pattern is completely made by Mother Nature.

Discovered on the seabed in the shallow tropical waters of Thailand and Indonesia, the gem is actually the protective door found at the opening of the Turban Snail's shell, which towards the end of the snail's natural life, detaches and sinks to the seabed. Although each spiral is similar in pattern, as with all organic gemstones, each one will vary slightly.

Across the gem rich countries of India, Tibet and Sri Lanka, many Hindu's worship the god Shiva. Many pictures of Shiva show a third eye in the middle of the god's forehead and it is from this that the gem's name is derived.

As with many shells the Shiva Eye is made of calcium carbonate. Although its body colour is always whitish, its beautiful swirl can vary in colour, depending on the snail's diet!

82

Signet Ring

Throughout history and until only 100 years ago, seals were used to provide authenticity to all sorts of transactions. From land deals to purchasing bales of hay, from property deals to barrels of wine, and even royal commitments to invitations, everything was authenticated with a seal. Even today some business transactions rely on a company seal, which is believed to be more authentic than a signature and in some countries the signet ring is still used for this purpose.

Even thousands of years ago (in the Bronze Age), Jews used seals and each of the twelve tribes of Israel had their own seal carved for them. A craftsman given the responsibility of creating these seals was regarded as a highly important person, who was not only the artist but also effectively acted as the librarian for each seal he created. Anyone who lost their personal seal ring was regarded as lowlife and it was said that they had lost not only their signet, but their personality too.

Many of the crowns of early signet rings were set with Peridot, Sardonyx and Jasper; these gemstones were not only highly valued, beautiful and strong, they were also not too difficult to carve.

Sillimanite

Sillimanite (also known as Fibrolite) is found in various colours including green, yellow, brown, blue, white and even black. It is a 'polymorph' with two other minerals, Kyanite and Andalusite, which simply means that it shares the same chemistry but has a different crystal structure.

Like Kyanite, this precious stone has a brittleness and directional cleavage that makes it difficult to facet. The scarcity of Sillimanite, combined with the difficulty in cutting it, adds incredible value to this gem once it has been successfully faceted.

The gem is a complete Jekyll and Hyde; it can be discovered as a truly transparent gem, or completely opaque with a waxy lustre. The gem's name was given in memory of geologist Benjamin Silliman.

It appears in deposits in several countries including Tanzania, South Africa, Korea, India, Madagascar, England and the USA. The rare transparent variety is mined in the Mogok Valley, Burma, where the deposit has also yielded some extremely rare violet-blue gems.

86

Silver

With big look jewellery now highly fashionable, Silver is often used by jewellers who prefer precious metal in their designs rather than simply using a coated base metal. Whilst less expensive than Gold, Silver is still a very costly alternative to base metals, so designs tend to incorporate hollow silver tubes and pressed pieces over casted components. As this precious metal is extremely pliable, beautiful intricate designs can be created. It also benefits from a wonderful lustre, a lustre which is so strong that it is used as a component in mirrors where a superior level of reflectivity is required!

What you may not know is that Silver is sometimes used as an alloy in Gold to turn it white. In 9k White Gold, it is possible for the Silver content to be of a higher level than the Gold (9k Gold has a minimum fineness of 37.5%, with 62.5% being made up of different alloys).

Another interesting fact about Silver is that for over 2700 years it has been used as a currency in many countries. So much so that the word for money and Silver is the same in at least 14 languages. The French word 'Argent' for example means both money and

Silver. As Silver is the best conductor of electricity - even better than copper - the biggest use of Silver today is in industry, with only 19% of all production being in jewellery and 6% being made into Silverware. That said, coins and medals still account for over 4% of the annual usage of Silver.

In the UK it is a legal requirement to hallmark all Silver items over 7.78 grams. There are four levels of fineness: 80% (hallmarked 800), 92.5% (hallmarked 925 and commonly known as Sterling Silver), 95.8% (hallmarked 958 and known as Britannia Silver) and 99.9%.

According to the 2007 British Geological Survey, Peru is the world's top producer of Silver, closely followed by Mexico. The next eight largest suppliers in descending order are; China, Chile, Australia, Poland, Russia, United States, Canada and Kazakhstan.

90

Sinhalite

If you are looking for something a little different, a gemstone that has real earthy colours that often looks like a crossbreed of Peridot and Smokey Quartz, a gemstone that's highly pleochroic and one that, as yet, I believe has not reached its full recognition in the gem world, then you might want to add Sinhalite to your collection.

The gem was first discovered in the Ratnapura District of Sri Lanka (previously known as Ceylon) and was at first thought to be an "off colour Peridot". In 1952 the gem was studied by two mineralogists, Claringbull and Hey, and found to be a new mineral, which was to be named after the Sanskrit word for Ceylon.

Sinhalite is an incredibly rare, collector's gemstone and in addition to the small deposit discovered in the gravel pits of Ratnapura, a handful of specimens have also been discovered in New Jersey, USA and in Tanzania. This is a very rare gemstone and a must for all serious collectors.

Smokey Quartz

Also known as Cairngorm Quartz after the Cairngorm Mountains of Scotland where it was once mined, Smokey Quartz is the national gemstone of Scotland

It is believed that Smokey Quartz helps to build a strong relationship and instill peace and harmony. It is thought to transform negative energy and is reported to be effective at dealing with anger.

Most Smokey Quartz coming out of the ground is not very consistent in colour and is therefore often heat-treated. In addition to Scotland, the gem has been discovered in Brazil, Germany, Australia, India, Madagascar and the USA.

93

94

Sodalite

You may think that you have yet to see a Sodalite, however if you have a piece of jewellery, an ornament or gemstone globe made of Lapis Lazuli much of its deep rich blue colour is most likely to be attributed to the mineral Sodalite. As well as being a vivid opaque blue gemstone, Sodalite is also the name given to the family of gemstones which includes Hackmanite and Lazurite.

Although the gemstone was initially discovered and documented in Greenland in 1806, it took a further century for a sufficient quantity to be unearthed in Ontario, Canada before it started to become faceted and set in jewellery.

The gem receives its name from the presence of sodium. It is sometimes also referred to as Princess Blue after Princess Patricia of Connaught fell so much in love with the gemstone whilst staying in Canada, that on her return to the UK she had whole areas of various rooms in Marlborough House decorated with Sodalite. Today gem quality Sodalite has been found in Australia, Brazil, Colombia.

Crystal healers believe that the gem can prove useful if you are in a state of mental confusion and that it is good for relieving stress. Sodalite is associated with the Chakras (especially the third eye) and is said to calm emotions and instill an inner peace.

South Africa

It seems hard to believe that the initial discovery of Diamonds in South Africa was made in December 1866 by 15 year old Erasmus Jacobs, who was out playing on his family's farm, 550 miles north-east of Capetown. The discovery was the catalyst for the "Great South African Diamond Rush", which turned a tiny little village known as Kimberley into a town of 50,000 people within a period of less than five years. Over the next ten years, South Africa became responsible for 95% of the world's Diamond supply. What was once regarded as the rarest gem on the planet was suddenly more widely available.

Although Diamonds were first discovered in India some 3000 to 4000 years ago, more Diamonds have been extracted from South Africa in 20 years than the entire amount ever recovered from Indian deposits!

The knowledge gained in South Africa led gem hunters to realise that Diamonds were likely to be discovered wherever distinct volcanic pipes could be found, leading them to explore other countries for the gemstone. These volcanic pipes are now known worldwide as Kimberlite pipes, after the small village in South Africa.

For twenty years after the initial discovery, there was continual, fierce rivalry for the control of the mines. In 1888, two of the largest mining companies owned by a Mr Rhodes and a Mr Barnato joined together and formed De Beers Consolidated Mines Ltd, who remain the largest supplier of Diamonds in the world until this day.

Outside of Diamond mining, South Africa is one of the world's largest producers of Tiger's Eye. Other than these two gemstones, very little else is mined in commercial quantities, other than a handful of small mines producing a limited amount of Emerald and Amethyst.

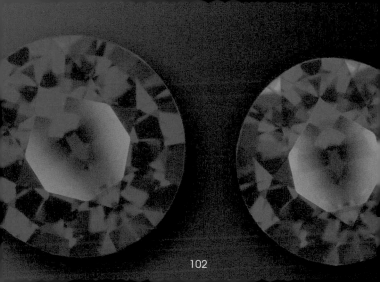

Spessartite Garnet

Spessartite Garnet is not the only orange Garnet, in fact there are two others: Hessonite and Malaya.

If you are evaluating an orange Garnet and it has great brilliance, as it has a slightly higher refractive index the chances are it is Spessartite (of all the popular coloured gemstones collected today, only Diamond and Zircon have a slightly higher refractive index). However, this is not a scientific test and for a conclusive identification it would be best to send your gem to a professional gem lab that would be able to identify its species by analysing its hardness (Spessartite measures 7.25 on the Mohs Scale which is more than both Hessonite and Malaya).

In terms of valuing a Spessartite, those with a pure hue, with little brown or yellow being visible, tend to fetch a higher price. That said, those that are a brownish orange are sometime re-labelled "burnt orange" and can often fetch a premium price. In terms of the perfect tone, a Spessartite with approximately 20 to 25% tone will have a beautiful open colour and maximum brilliance.

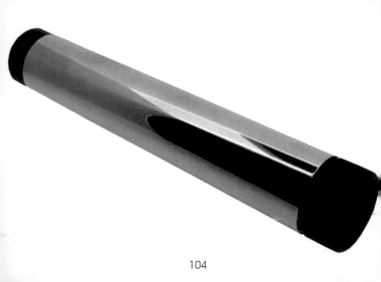

Spectrometer

Before we discuss how a Spectrometer works and how to use it, lets first look at when to use. Whilst the Refractometer is brilliant at measuring the refractive index (RI) of a gemstone, it does have several limitations. First of all it only useful for gems that are cut and polished, if a gem is in its rough state (as it comes out of the ground), the Refractometer can not get an accurate reading. Also, if the gem has a very high refractive index, then the Refractometer use is limited. And of course for gemstones that are set into jewellery, if they are too large to fit into the Refractometer, then it physically

not possible to use this equipment. That said, don't be put of by these three exceptions because a Refractometer, is still one of the easiest tools and most accurate ways of identifying most cut gemstones.

So when do you use your Spectrometer? Well in addition to the aforementioned scenarios, its always best when trying to identify a gemstone to double check any of your findings with secondary tests. As gemstones are a product of nature, where there are always exceptions and slight difference in composition, professional laboratory gemologists will never rely on the findings of just one piece of equipment and will always back up any of their findings with several different tests.

How does a Spectrometer work? Where as the Refractometer measures the refraction of light, the Spectrometer analyses light as it passes through a gemstone. As white light travels through a gem, one or more of the wavelengths (all colours have different wavelengths) are absorbed. As you will remember from school, white light is made up of different colours, but of course when we look at a white light all we see is white, humans do not have the ability to see the different colours that make up white light. If we did, then we would not need a Spectrometer, as we would simply study our gemstones and see which colours were absorbed and lost within the gem. All gemstones have different optical phenomena and the Spectrometers job is to measure the selective absorption of the gem being analysed. Some gemstones have a very clear and defined characteristic and are easily detected with a Spectrometer, and others do not.

When you shine a white light through the end of your Spectrometer and look through the eye piece at the other end (first without a gemstone) you will vibrantly see the colours of the rainbow all in order; red, orange, yellow, green, blue, indigo, violet.

Now if we insert a gemstone between the light source, if it is a gemstone that absorbs a certain wavelength (colour), then you will see a black line in the eye piece where the gemstone has stolen the colour.

Obviously, because it is measuring light as it travels through the gem, it is one of the few pieces of equipment for example that can identify if a coloured Diamond is natural or treated.

Whilst there are lots of different types of spectrometers in use in different fields of science, there are two main types of spectrometer used in gemology. In professional laboratories there is one known as a Prism Spectrometer, however as these are more expensive they are rarely used by hobbyists and Gem Collectors.

108

Sphalerite

The most amazing thing about collecting coloured gemstones is that Mother Nature never fails to shock you. Until February this year, all I knew about Sphalerite was that the Smithsonian Museum of Natural History and the Liverpool World Museum had samples of this mineral; I had never contemplated setting the mineral in jewellery and had therefore not included it in the first edition of these books.

Then over dinner one day, a very good friend of mine told me he had recently seen a specimen that was bright orange and that it had an amazing amount of dispersion. The next day I spent several hours on the internet researching the gem type and was amazed at what I found. My friend's observation of a strong amount of fire was very accurate indeed: the gem has a dispersion that is over three times that of a Diamond (technically speaking it has a B-G interval of 0.156)!

Sphalerite consists mainly of Zinc and Iron. Normally the Iron content dominates and the mineral looks similar to the dull pieces seen in the museums. Most Sphalerite is opaque

110

and black and is sometimes referred to as Marmatite (was this the origin of our Marmite spread or was it a French stew?). Isn't the gem world so exciting, when the graphite in your pencil has the exact same chemical composition as a Diamond (see allotropic) and dull old Marmatite is the same mineral as the most incredibly dazzling and monumentally rare Sphalerite! To my knowledge only a handful of yellow, orange and red specimens have been found so far and nearly all are below 1ct.

Only two mines have ever been reported to discover gem quality pieces; the Chivera mine, in Sonora Mexico and the Las Manforas Mine in the Picos de Europa Montains (the first national park in Spain) located on the North Coast of Spain near Santander. Its name is derived from the Greek word for 'treacherous rock', as non-gem quality specimens can easily be confused with other minerals. The gem is also known as Blende which is the German word for 'blind' (most likely so for the same reason as the Greek meaning).

Sphene

Sphene is one of the newest gemstones to be discovered, taking its name from the Greek word for "wedge" - due to its typical wedge-shaped crystal structure. It is sometimes known as "Titanite", due to its titanium content. Its colour is generally green, yellow or darkish grey, yet in some forms it can also be brown and even black.

Registering 5.5 on the Mohs scale, the softness of the stone makes it difficult to facet; but because it is so beautiful, many Lapidarists are often tempted to give it a go. The gem is transparent to translucent in appearance and can often feature the most amazing adamantine lustre. Sphene also has fire (dispersion) greater than that of even Diamonds and is therefore ideal when set in earrings or pendants that are designed to be fluid. Its double refraction enables the light that travels through the gem to be split into two directions, creating an exceptional array of colours. Strongly coloured Sphenes are also heavily pleochroic. The gemstone is mined in Pakistan, Mount Vesuvius, Italy, Russia, Canada and the USA.

114

Spice Topaz

Spice Topaz uses a revolutionary patented technique to add spectacular colours to genuine Topaz. With 12 colours to choose from and with a continual research program to develop more, Spice Topaz offers a range of coloured gemstones unlike any seen before. Choose from Summer Blue, Aqua, Liberty Blue, True Blue, Neon Paraiba, Padparadscha Sunset, Pristine, Deep Sage, Fern Green, Diva Green, Peru and Dusky Black.

Using exactly the same colouring agents that Mother Nature uses to add colour to allochromatic gems, Spice Topaz uses its revolutionary and entirely safe process to penetrate colour deep inside the gem. Since the importing of Topaz with radiation treatment was banned in the USA, some American jewellers now only offer Spice Topaz (alongside very rare untreated pieces) and the owner of one store recently told me that the only difficulty consumers now face is which of the 12 brilliant colours to choose from.

The technical stuff: why did two scientists spend years developing and patenting Spice Topaz? Well to understand this you need to understand

the limitations of other techniques used to add colour to Topaz. Mystic coating can be damaged if not properly looked after. Radiation treatment of Topaz has had a rocky road in the USA over its potential health hazards. Regular diffusion does not penetrate deep into the gem and can therefore be negatively affected by small chips and scratches, plus it is not very effective when used with Topaz. However Spice Topaz diffuses colour deep into the gemstone and is 100% stable and totally permanent.

118

Spinel

We all hate doing nasty jobs and often procrastinate when we have to deliver bad news, but who can imagine how difficult it must have been telling the Queen of Great Britain that her beloved Ruby in the crown jewels was not a Ruby at all, but a lesser known gem; a Spinel!

Spinel is a robust and strong gem for gents to wear. The "Black Prince's Ruby", which was set into Henry V's helmet, saved his life when his helmet was struck by an axe in the battle of Agincourt in 1415. This only goes to show how certain gemstones are far stronger than the precious metals into which they are set. For hundreds of years Spinels have been mistaken for Rubies. The "Black Prince's Ruby", which is now set in the British Imperial State Crown, was thought by Henry V to be a Ruby (hence its name); but it is actually a 170ct Spinel. The "Kuwait Ruby", another piece in the British crown jewels, is also a Spinel; weighing a massive 352ct.

It is easy to understand why Spinels were mistaken for Rubies for so long. In fact, until the late 19th century, there was no distinction between Ruby and Red Spinel, as they look almost identical and are often found in the same localities. They also share the same desirable visual properties, as well as similar chemical structure, and both even obtain their red colour from chromium. This is how red Spinel obtained its title as "The Master of Disguise".

Nowadays, distinctions can be made through comparing the hardness of the two gemstones: Ruby registers 9 on the Mohs scale, while Spinel registers 8. Ruby also has a slightly higher refractive index. Most Spinels also have the ability to glow in natural daylight (fluorescence) but with a more pinkish hue than Rubies.

Red Spinel is actually rarer than Ruby, but unlike the latter can be found in large sizes. These big red stones were often referred to in ancient texts as Balas Rubies, which referred to Badakshan in Northern Afghanistan - still an active gem producing region. According to historical records, Badakshan produced the biggest and most spectacular "Rubies". Some of these gems were owned by the Mongol conqueror Gengis Khan, Henry VIII of England, and Peter the Great of Russia.

Spinel's name is believed to have

derived from the Latin word "spina" meaning "thorn" and refers to the fact that its crystals are often shaped like the thorns of a rose bush. Along the same theme, its vivid colours are often very similar to those seen in an English rose garden. Pure Spinel is white and, as with many gem families, its impurities provide us with an array of different colours. The main colouring agents in Spinel are iron, chromium, vanadium and cobalt. Not only can this precious gem be found in beautiful rich Ruby reds; a very small amount has been found in electrifying blues. You can also find a range of pastel colours of purples and pinks. One of the most spectacular gemstone colours, vivid hot pink with a hint of orange, can be found in Spinels mined in Burma.

Though most Spinels on the market don't have prefixes, several trade names do exist. Flame Spinel (also known as Rubicelle) as the name suggests is a vivacious orange to orangey red gem. Ceylonite (also known as Pleonaste) is an opaque dark green Spinel, and Gahnite (also known as Zinc Spinel) is a blue to bluish green Spinel.

Because this crystal is a newly recognised gemstone there is little folklore and legend surrounding its powers, although it has been associated with sorcerers and alchemists alike.

There is reference to its use as a talisman to protect the wearer from fire, and as Spinel contains the magnetic mineral Magnetite, many believe it was used to help ancient mariners with navigation.

In 2005, whilst conducting a scientific study at the University of Chicago, Denton Ebel (Assistant Curator of Meteorites at the American Museum of Natural History), along with Lawrence Grossman (a Professor in Geophysical Sciences), discovered that the environment in which certain Spinels were formed proved that it was the impact of an asteroid some 65 million years ago that ended the dinosaur era.

Now treasured in its own right, Spinel is a favourite of many gem dealers and Gem Collectors. It has fantastic brilliance with a vitreous lustre, and as it is very durable and tough, it makes it an ideal gem to set into jewellery. It is mined in Burma, Sri Lanka, India, Tanzania, Madagascar, Australia, Italy, Sweden, Turkey, United States and Russia.

Spodumene

What an unfortunate name for a gemstone family that heralds such beautiful gems as Kunzite and Hiddenite Its name is derived from "spondumenos" which is Greek for "burnt to ashes" and came about due to the similarity that some Spodumene specimens have with the greyish appearance of ash. All members of the Spodumene family are highly plechroic.

Even though Spodumene is rarely set in jewellery itself, its three descendants Kunzite, Green Hiddenite and (the more recently discovered) transparent yellow Triphane are amongst some of the most desirable gems on the planet. This last gem, Triphane, should not be confused with the sleeping agent tryptophan which is found in its most concentrated form in turkeys - hence the real reason you fall asleep after Christmas dinner.

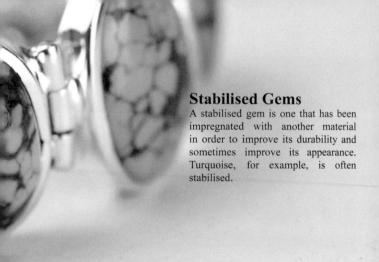

Stabilised Gems

A stabilised gem is one that has been impregnated with another material in order to improve its durability and sometimes improve its appearance. Turquoise, for example, is often stabilised.

Star Sapphire

A Star Sapphire is a Sapphire that has a pattern within the stone that emits a star-like effect known as asterism.

A skilled cutter will be able to determine from the rough if a Sapphire is likely to possess the star effect, which is not visible to the naked eye before cutting. The value of the gem will always depend upon how close the star is to the centre of the gem, its clarity, and the depth of colour of the Sapphire. Most stars witnessed on the surface of Sapphires have four prongs; however, in the rarest of cases a six-prong star can be seen, making the gemstone a truly collectible item.

You will find that a Star Sapphire is always cabochon cut, with its dome allowing the asterism to shine through; if it were cut in any other shape the star would be lost.

Star India

The Star of India is said to be the largest and most famous Sapphire in the world! It was discovered in Ceylon in the early 1700's and is believed to have formed over a billion years ago.

Its home is now in the New York Museum of Natural History: it was presented to them by the financier J.P Morgan in 1900. In appearance the Star of India looks quite milky. It receives its star effect (also known as asterism) from the presence of tiny rutile inclusions which all run parallel to one another within the gemstone. The gem weighs a huge 563cts and is similar in size to a ping pong ball.

Like many of the world's famous Diamonds, this Sapphire is surrounded by scandal. In 1964 the Star of India was the object of a famous burglary when it was stolen by Jack Murphy (also known as 'Murph the Surf'). Although he was arrested within a few days, the Sapphire wasn't recovered for several months and was allegedly discovered in a locker in a Miami bus station.

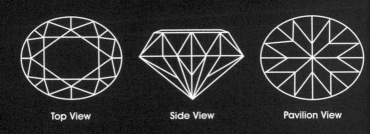

Top View   **Side View**   **Pavilion View**

Star of the South

This famous Diamond was discovered in 1853 by a young girl who was a slave working at the Bagagem Diamond Mine in Brazil. At the time it was a custom that anyone finding a Diamond of great significance would be granted freedom and on unearthing a huge Diamond which weighed over 250cts in its rough state, the girl was apparently not only set free but also given a pension for life. The owner of the mine had little idea of its true value and it is reported that he sold the gem for around £3,000, only for the new owner to sell it for 10 times more just a few months later!

Also known as Estreal do Sul, the Star of the South is today a 128.48ct beautifully cushion cut, VS2 clarity Diamond that is light pink in colour. The Diamond has enjoyed a very eventful and well documented history over the past 100 years and in 2002 Cartier purchased it from Rustomjee Jamsetjee of Mumbai. Not long after their purchase, the Diamond became subject to a legal case as it was claimed to be listed as an heirloom of the wealthy Gaekwad family.

I find the cut of this gem as impressive as the gem itself. Therefore we have recently had two of our head Lapidaries develop our "Replica Star".

134

St. Edward's Crown

Although throughout history there have been two crowns known as 'St Edward's Crown', the one currently on exhibition in the Tower of London dates back to 1661 and was produced the year after the restoration of the monarchy.

The crown is used at the coronation ceremony and is placed on the head of the incoming monarch by the Archbishop of Canterbury. However, due to its incredible weight of 2.23kg, both King George VI and Elizabeth II replaced it with the lighter weight and more comfortable Imperial State Crown before leaving the Abbey at the end of the coronation.

Made of solid gold, such was the cost of precious gemstones at the time that the crown only featured hired gems, rented from jewellers several weeks before the coronation and given back afterwards.

From the coronation of Queen Anne in 1702 until the early 19th century, the crown was not actually worn by the incoming king or queens (not surprising as it was so heavy), but was carried separately to the ceremony as a symbolic object. In 1902, Edward VII decided that he would wear the crown for his coronation and commissioned

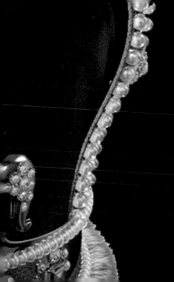

its restoration. However, on the day of his coronation Edward was suffering with appendicitis and was unable to wear the hefty crown!

Prior to the coronation of George V in 1911, Garrard the Crown Jewellers were employed for the first time in the crown's history to permanently set over 400 genuine gemstones. According to "The Official Guide Book – The Crown Jewels", Garrards were responsible for 'removing the antique enamelled mounts, all the pastes (stones) and resetting them with semi precious stones'. These included Amethysts, Sapphires, Tourmalines, Topaz and Citrines.

137

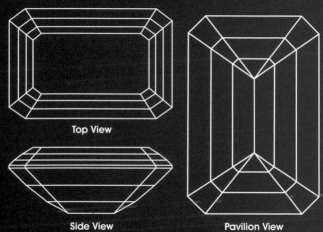

Top View

Side View

Pavilion View

Step Cut

It's best to imagine brilliant cuts and step cuts as two different families, in which most styles of cuts fall into. Whereas brilliant cuts tend to have triangular and kite-shaped facets, step cuts tend to have rectangular facets. The emerald cut, for example, falls into the step cut family.

Step cuts have facets that run parallel to the table, tend to have two or more steps cut onto the crown angling towards the table, and normally have more steps faceted below the girdle on the pavillion. With a larger gem, more steps will often be used. If you are unsure of what type of cut you are looking at, if the table facet looks square, rectangular, hexagonal or octagonal, then the chances are that it is a step cut gem.

**Stephen
Whittard**

STEPHEN WHITTARD

142

Sterling Silver

Like 9K Gold and 18K Gold, the British Assay Office have a certain standard which must be reached in order for Sterling Silver to be named as such: more than 92.5% of the metal must be pure Silver. In America, Sterling Silver only needs to be 92.1% pure to achieve its status. The reason Sterling Silver is made into an alloy is that, on its own, silver is a fairly soft metal and therefore copper is normally added to the blend to make it stronger.

The term "Sterling Silver," emerged in the 13th century and it is no coincidence that the British currency is also called Sterling. Interestingly, in French, the word "argent" also means both Silver and money. Another Silver standard is Britannia. This is purer than Sterling and to achieve its official hallmark at least 95.84% of the alloy needs to be Silver. However, as it is softer than Sterling Silver it is not used as often in jewellery.

In the UK it is a legal requirement for retailers to ensure that all Silver items that weigh in excess of 7.78 grams have an official hallmark. Be careful though, as most manufacturers will stamp 925 on the Silver jewellery they produce and this should not to be confused with the official hallmark applied by the Assay Office.

• Sterling Silver

144

• Sterling Silver

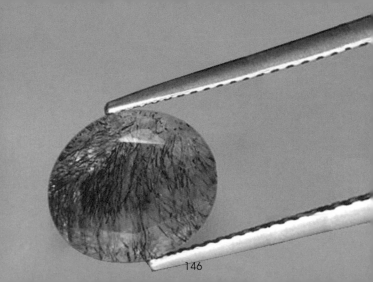

146

Strawberry Quartz

Found in only a few locations, Strawberry Quartz receives its unique colouring through Haematite and Lepidocrocite inclusions. Many people have wrongly mistaken Strawberry Quartz for Quenched Crackle Quartz, but under closer examination, it becomes apparent that Strawberry Quartz is completely natural. Also, it's worth pointing out that the name has been incorrectly used by several jewellers who are selling glass and passing it off as a gemstone!

Depending on the location where each gemstone has so far been found, the gemstone has different visual qualities. Those sold so far at The Genuine Gemstones Company have all been from Madagascar and are 100% natural, without treatment, without enhancement and without heating! They are truly a miracle produced by Mother Nature.

This find that we have is from a big open pit mine. We have sourced a lot of material from this mine: most of it is opaque and only has black spots; less than 4% of the material appears transparent and has the strawberry coloured spots. The only problem is, we have to continually cut away at

the less attractive material to reach the fascinating gem quality Strawberry Quartz.

For a gemstone whose availability is so scant, because of its unusual appearance, it has already received a lot interest from crystal healers and astrologists. Strawberry Quartz is said to 'stimulate the energy of the heart filling one with the feeling of love'.

Sugilite

Sometimes referred to as "Royal Lavulite" or "Royal Azel", Sugilite appears in a small range of colours from a stunning light lavender through to a rich purple. It is opaque with a waxy lustre and its appearance always reminds me of the small round violet sweets I was given as a child. The gem received its name from a Dr Ken-ichi Sugi, a Japanese scientist who first documented the gemstone in the 1940's.

Sugilite occasionally features red, brown or yellow spots, when these are present the gem is often called Wild Horse Sugilite. Similar to the process used to stabilise Turquoise, the gem is often treated to make it more suitable for setting in jewellery.

Some crystal healers believe that Sugilite helps in strengthening the heart, as well as reducing levels of stress, whilst others suggest that it balances your mind, body and spirit. I was recently told that a friend's mother uses Sugilite to stop her from developing a negative outlook on life and for over four years she has been more at ease and better equipped to deal with the troubles she watches on the evening news.

152

Sunstone

This gemstone has a gorgeous glittering appearance (known as aventurescence) and is also called Oligoclase, Aventurine Feldspar and Heliote. Sunstone has many sought after attributes, but its aventuresence is the most striking. This is usually caused by either Haematite or Goethite inclusions; but in the Sunstone from Oregon in the USA, this phenomenon owes its appearance to copper inclusions. Although its colour is normally a reddish brown, it has also been discovered in green, grey, and yellow.

The gem has been set in jewellery for thousands of years and is steeped in history and folklore. The Vikings were said to have used the gem as a navigational aid, whilst early American settlers ground the gem and used it in medicine.

Sunstone is a member of the Feldspar family and is closely related to Labradorite. As it is normally opaque or translucent the gem is often cabochon cut; on rare occasions it can be found transparent.

The gem registers 6 to 6.5 on the Mohs scale and can be found in Norway, Canada, India and the USA.

Switzerland

Without doubt when it comes to watch manufacturing, Switzerland is the undisputed world champion. Even though many well-known brand names are moving their watch production to Asia, the very patriotic Swiss are still making their watches in their wonderfully landscaped and land locked country.

In a world that is changing so rapidly, there is still something magical about owning a Swiss watch. Although very few people can afford a true Swiss watch, in second place come watches bearing the engraving or label "Swiss

Movement". When you see this on a watch it does not necessarily mean the watch is made in Switzerland, but refers to the provenance of the mechanism within the watch.

Just like the French who protect the use of the name "Champagne", the Swiss have fought hard recently to ban companies from abbreviating "Swiss Movement" to "Swiss Movt", in an attempt to protect the authenticity of the genuine Swiss watch makers. When it comes to mining, Switzerland has several Gold deposits, glorious Marcasite and small deposits of gem quality Quartz, Prehnite, Unakite, Idocrase and Haematite.

With the exception of its Gold and Marcasite mining activities, it is important to stress that Switzerland's other gems are not really mined in commercial quantities.

High in the Alps in the Canton of Valais, very near the Italian border, some of the most fantastic Marcasite in the world is being mined. Its colours range from creamy to glorious, metallic golden tones with a pale rose tint. The mine has been in operation for over 100 years and, as with most things in Switzerland, runs like clockwork!

In my humble opinion, no other Marcasite on the planet has the same quality of lustre and surface integrity to that which is mined in the Swiss Canton of Valais. My view is not clouded by the fact that I spend a fair amount of time in Switzerland overseeing our Lorique watchmaking, it's simply because the gem is truly amazing.

One gem that is not mined in Switzerland is Swiss Blue Topaz. This trade name is generically applied to Blue Topaz that are of strong clarity and medium dark in colour. Lighter Blue Topaz is referred to as Sky Blue Topaz and dark Blue Topaz is often named London Blue.